THESEUS
BATTLING THE MINOTAUR

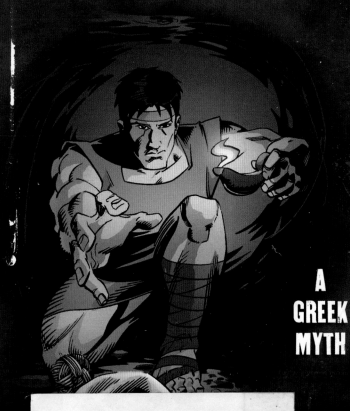

A GREEK MYTH

GRAPHIC UNIVERSE™

STORY BY
JEFF LIMKE

PENCILS AND INKS BY
JOHN McCREA

EUROPE

ITALY

MEDITERRANEAN SEA

THESEUS
BATTLING THE MINOTAUR

A
GREEK
MYTH

BLACK SEA

TURKEY

GREECE

AEGEAN SEA

ATHENS

CRETE

LERNER BOOKS · LONDON · NEW YORK · MINNEAPOLIS

Theseus is one of the greatest heroes of Greek mythology. His feats of strength and courage have been passed down from generation to generation for more than 2000 years. This particular book follows Theseus' early adventures, as he comes of age and attempts to fulfill his destiny as a great hero and Athens' greatest king. To craft this tale for the Graphic Myths and Legends series, author Jeff Limke consulted two of the most famous anthologies of Greek myths, Edith Hamilton's *Mythology* and *Bulfinch's Mythology* by Thomas Bulfinch. Artist John McCrea referenced numerous historical and traditional sources to give the art an authentic look, from classical Greek architecture to the clothing, weapons and armour worn by the characters. Professor David Mulroy ensured historical and visual accuracy.

STORY BY JEFF LIMKE

PENCILS AND INKS BY JOHN McCREA

COLOURING BY HI-FI COLOUR DESIGN

LETTERING BY HI-FI COLOUR DESIGN

CONSULTANT: DAVID MULROY, PHD
UNIVERSITY OF WISCONSIN-MILWAUKEE

Graphic Universe™ is a trademark of Lerner Publishing Group, Inc.

First published in the United Kingdom in 2009 by
Lerner Books,
Dalton House,
60 Windsor Avenue,
London SW19 2RR

Website address: www.lernerbooks.co.uk

This edition was updated and edited for UK publication by Discovery Books Ltd., First Floor, 2 College Street, Ludlow, Shropshire SY8 1AN

British Library Cataloguing in Publication Data

Limke, Jeff
Theseus : battling the Minotaur. - 2nd ed. - (Graphic universe)
1. Theseus (Greek mythology) - Comic books, strips, etc. - Juvenile fiction 2. Minotaur (Greek mythology) - Comic books, strips, etc. - Juvenile fiction 3. Children's stories - Comic books, strips, etc.
I. Title II. McCrea, John, artist/creator
741.5

ISBN-13: 978 0 7613 4351 6

Printed in Singapore

TABLE OF CONTENTS

THE TREASURE
BENEATH THE BOULDER

MY NAME IS *CONNIDUS* AND I TAUGHT *THESEUS* AS A CHILD. I TAUGHT HIM HISTORY, POETRY AND MATHEMATICS. HIS MOTHER *AETHRA* TAUGHT HIM WHAT HE NEEDED TO KNOW TO BECOME KING. WHAT HE NEEDED TO LEARN TO BECOME ONE OF GREECE'S GREATEST HEROES, HE WOULD HAVE TO LEARN ON HIS OWN.

WHEN HE WAS OLD ENOUGH, HIS MOTHER TOLD HIM THAT THE FIRST OF MANY TASKS HE WOULD HAVE TO PERFORM WOULD BE TO MOVE THE BOULDER THAT STOOD AT THE TOP OF THE HILL ABOVE THE CAVE WHERE HE LIVED.

WHAT SHE DIDN'T TELL HIM WAS THAT HIS FATHER WAS THE CURRENT KING OF ATHENS. INSTEAD SHE HAD TOLD HIM HE WAS THE SON OF *POSEIDON,* THE GOD OF THE SEA.

THE TREASURE BENEATH THE ROCK WAS *NOT* WHAT HE HAD EXPECTED.

THESEUS—

YES, GRANDFATHER PITTHEUS?

YOU KNOW THERE ARE TWO WAYS TO ATHENS. THE SEA WILL BE SAFER AND FASTER.

OVER LAND WILL BE LONGER AND MORE DANGEROUS.

HERAKLES*, THE GREATEST HERO, CHALLENGED THE DANGERS AND SUCCEEDED.

IF I'M TO BE A HERO AND ONE DAY A KING, THERE CAN BE ONLY ONE CHOICE.

*BETTER KNOWN BY HIS ROMAN NAME HERCULES

NO, PLEASE GO BY SEA. IT WILL BE DANGEROUS ENOUGH.

I CAN TAKE CARE OF MYSELF.

DO NOT WORRY, MOTHER AND GRANDFATHER.

BANDITS ON THE ROAD

Theseus left his home in the mountains and began his journey.

He knew he would have to face challenges. He also knew he had to beat them if he was going to be worthy of becoming king.

In truth, he couldn't *wait* to prove himself.

He didn't have to wait long.

KA-BOOM!

Well, well, well, what do I have here? A boy dressed like he wants to be a hero.

You have the shield, but you're missing something. A *sword*, perhaps?

Or maybe...

A club?

KA-BOOM!

THESEUS HAD NOT GONE MUCH FURTHER WHEN *ANOTHER BANDIT APPEARED, SINIS THE PINEBENDER.*

EXCUSE ME, TRAVELLER, BUT I'M AFRAID YOU CAN GO NO FURTHER.

WHY WOULD THAT BE? THE ROAD IS CLEAR.

TRUE. BUT THOSE WHO HAVE GONE FORWARD PASSED A SIMPLE TEST.

SIMPLY PROVE YOU CAN HOLD THIS TREETOP AND ONE OTHER. IF YOU ARE STRONG ENOUGH, YOU CAN GO ON—

—OTHERWISE YOU WILL HAVE TO FIND A DIFFERENT ROUTE, AN EASIER ROUTE.

HAND ME THE BRANCH.

TH-THERE.

NOT BAD.

BUT YOU'RE NOT FINISHED. MANY HAVE DONE THAT. BUT FEW HAVE ACCOMPLISHED WHAT COMES NEXT.

creak-crack

creak-crack

WOULD YOU LET ME RE-GRIP THIS ONE, FIRST? I WAS NOT READY TO HOLD TWO.

I'M SURE YOU CAN GUESS WHAT I'M GOING TO ASK OF YOU.

OF COURSE.

ZAZING!

TAKE AS LONG AS YOU NEED. IT MAKES NO DIFFERENCE.

EITHER YOU WILL BE ABLE TO DO IT—

—OR YOU WILL *NOT*.

13

HAVING VANQUISHED TWO BANDITS, THESEUS KNEW THAT ATHENS COULD NOT BE FAR AWAY.

GOOD TRAVELLER, I AM *PROCRUSTES* AND THIS IS MY INN.

HOW FAR IS IT TO ATHENS?

WHY DON'T YOU JUST STAY HERE?

IF YOU'RE LIKE MY PAST TRAVELLERS, YOU'LL FIND WE'RE JUST THE RIGHT SIZE.

FROM HERE TO ATHENS IT WILL TAKE A STRONG MAN OF YOUR HEIGHT A GOOD FULL DAY OF WALKING.

I THINK YOU'RE RIGHT. YOUR INN LOOKS TAILOR-MADE FOR ME.

I COULDN'T AGREE MORE.

GO ON THROUGH THERE WITH YOUR BELONGINGS.

PLEASE MAKE SURE EVERYTHING IS SUITABLE.

THANK YOU, I WILL.

HOW ARE THINGS?

THE BED LOOKS BIG ENOUGH.

I THOUGHT IT MIGHT.

I'LL SEE WHAT I CAN DO ABOUT THAT.

I WOULDN'T WORRY ABOUT IT IF I WERE YOU.

I'M SURE I'LL BE JUST FINE.

IT'S NOT A PROBLEM, I ASSURE YOU.

THAT'S GOOD. NO NEED TO GO TO ANY TROUBLE FOR ME.

AFTER THEY HAD EATEN, *THESEUS* FELT THE DAY HAD CAUGHT UP TO HIM.

I'M TIRED, PROCRUSTES. I THINK I'LL GO TO BED.

CAN YOU WAKE ME AT SUNRISE? I WANT TO GET TO ATHENS AS EARLY AS I CAN.

I CAN DO THAT. THE COCKEREL WILL WAKE YOU REGARDLESS.

LATER THAT EVENING WHEN THE MOON WAS HIGH.

IT'S TIME TO MAKE SURE YOU FIT THIS—

WHAT?

WHERE IS HE?

KA-KLONK!

P-P-LEASE LET...ME...

...G-GO.

NO. THIS IS WHAT YOU WOULD HAVE DONE TO ME.

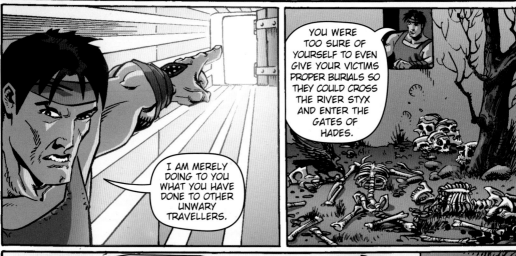

I AM MERELY DOING TO YOU WHAT YOU HAVE DONE TO OTHER UNWARY TRAVELLERS.

YOU WERE TOO SURE OF YOURSELF TO EVEN GIVE YOUR VICTIMS PROPER BURIALS SO THEY COULD CROSS THE RIVER STYX AND ENTER THE GATES OF HADES.

BE GLAD YOU WERE TOO SHORT OR I WOULD HAVE USED THE SWORD YOU USED TO MAKE TALLER TRAVELLERS FIT.

YOU MADE YOUR BED, *PROCRUSTES*-

-NOW, YOU CAN SLEEP IN IT!

THE KING OF ATHENS

SEND A MESSENGER TO THE PALACE! A LONE MAN CARRYING A WEAPON APPROACHES.

MAKE WAY, I HAVE AN URGENT MESSAGE FOR THE KING!

WHAT NEWS DO YOU BRING ME?

A LONE TRAVELLER ARRIVES!

THAT IS NOT NEWS!

BUT THIS TRAVELLER CARRIES A WEAPON OF ONE OF THE BANDITS KNOWN TO LIVE ON THE ROAD TO ATHENS.

THIS I MUST SEE.

TAKE ME TO SEE HIM.

YOU SPOKE THE TRUTH.

THIS MAN COULD BE THE PERSON WHO COULD UNITE ATHENS BEHIND ME.

BRING HIM TO ME IMMEDIATELY.

YOU WILL COME WITH US. *KING AEGEUS* DEMANDS TO SPEAK WITH YOU.

WHY?

LET ME GIVE YOU SOME ADVICE, *COUNTRY BOY*–

–WHEN YOU'RE KING, *YOU* CAN ASK QUESTIONS.

TELL ME YOUR NAME, BOY.

MY MOTHER NAMED ME *THESEUS.*

AND THIS CLUB? IT BELONGED TO *CORYNETES* DIDN'T IT?

YES. IT'S MINE NOW.

I DON'T THINK HE'LL BE BOTHERING ANY MORE TRAVELLERS.

SO I HEAR. MY SOLDIERS TELL ME YOU HAVE MADE TRAVEL SAFE ON THAT ROAD.

YOU HAVE MY THANKS.

THAT SIGN ON THE SHIELD IS THE SAME AS *AEGEUS'.*

THESEUS IS *KING AEGEUS'* SON.

YOU'RE A GUEST IN MY PALACE.

MEDEA WAS NOT HAPPY. SHE HAD MARRIED AEGEUS BELIEVING HE HAD NO CHILDREN. SHE HOPED HER CHILDREN COULD BECOME THE RULERS OF ATHENS. THESEUS' ARRIVAL SURELY THREATENED HER PLAN.

AEGEUS, I THINK YOU NEED TO FEAR THIS THESEUS.

IF HE CAN DEFEAT THE BANDITS, YOU KNOW HE COULD REPLACE YOU IN THE PEOPLE'S HEARTS.

YOU PROMISED MY SONS THEY COULD RULE ATHENS AFTER YOU.

WHAT WOULD YOU HAVE ME DO?

HE IS A GUEST IN MY HOME.

IF THIS THESEUS WERE TO DO SOMETHING TO YOU, THEY AREN'T READY.

IT IS INTOLERABLE FOR A HOST TO HARM HIS GUEST.

PERHAPS, BUT HE ISN'T MY GUEST.

YOU JUST LET ME WORRY ABOUT THESEUS.

YOU WORRY ABOUT RULING.

LATER, **AEGEUS** INVITED THE NOBLES TO A GREAT BANQUET TO TALK, TO EAT AND TO INTRODUCE THEM TO THE YOUNG HERO WHO HAD MADE THE ROAD SAFE.

YOUNG **THESEUS.** WHO ARE YOUR PARENTS, AGAIN?

I DIDN'T KNOW MY FATHER. I WAS TOLD IT WAS **POSEIDON,** BUT HE HAS NEVER VISITED ME.

BUT MY MOTHER'S NAME WAS—

—AETHRA

SAY THAT NAME AGAIN, BOY!

AETHRA?

DON'T LET HIM DRINK THAT—

—AND BRING HIM TO ME!

23

IN *AEGEUS'* CHAMBERS, *THESEUS* TOLD HIS TALE.

—AND NOW I'M HERE TO MEET MY FATHER AND CLAIM MY BIRTHRIGHT.

YOU ARE MY SON, *THESEUS.*

YOU SHALL RULE THIS CITY SOMEDAY.

ALREADY I HAVE HEARD YOUR NAME MENTIONED AMONG MY GUARDS.

YOUR ADVENTURES ON THE ROADS HAVE IMPRESSED THEM AND THAT IS NOT EASILY DONE.

THOSE BANDITS WERE LITTLE PEOPLE WHO DESERVED NO MORE THAN WHAT I GAVE THEM.

BEING A RULER IS SIMILAR.

THE REWARD SEEMS BETTER.

PERHAPS. EVEN AS WE TALK, OTHERS CONSPIRE AGAINST ME.

THERE ARE GROUPS WITHIN THE CITY THAT WOULD LIKE TO STEAL MY THRONE.

IT IS ALL I CAN DO TO RULE MY CITY.

PERHAPS OUR YOUNG HERO COULD HELP ME.

THERE IS ALWAYS OUR AGREEMENT WITH CRETE.

NO, I WILL NOT DO THAT.

TELL ME MORE.

THE BOY SHOULD KNOW, AEGEUS.

VERY WELL.

EVERY YEAR WE SEND SEVEN BOYS AND SEVEN GIRLS SO CRETE WILL NOT WAGE WAR AGAINST US.

I DO NOT LIKE DOING THIS, BUT WE WOULD LOSE MORE LIVES IF KING MINOS ATTACKED US AS HE DID BEFORE THIS AGREEMENT.

WE HEAR TALES OF WHAT HAPPENS TO THEM, BUT NO ONE HAS EVER RETURNED ALIVE TO TELL US FOR SURE.

MY SONS ARE TOO YOUNG, BUT YOU—

—YOU COULD BE THE HERO TO END THIS TERRIBLE THING.

INCLUDE ME WITH THIS OFFERING.

I CAN END THIS!

PUT ME ON THE SHIP. I AM NOT TOO OLD TO DO THIS.

LET THE PEOPLE KNOW I AM GOING.

THEY WILL KNOW YOU ARE ONE OF THEM BY SACRIFICING YOUR ONLY SON.

BUT YOU HAVE JUST RETURNED. I CAN'T SEND YOU AWAY NOW.

YOU MUST. I CAN UNITE THE PEOPLE FOR YOU—

—FOR US.

25

AND SO THE SHIP SAILED FOR THE ISLAND OF CRETE'S CAPITAL, *KNOSSOS*, RULED BY *KING MINOS*.

KING MINOS AND THE MINOTAUR

When the ship arrived, **King Minos** was waiting.

TOO SMALL.

TOO SKINNY.

TOO FAT.

TOO WEAK.

AH, THAT ONE LOOKS FINE.

I WANT HIM.

WHAT IS YOUR NAME, BOY?

THESEUS.

ADDRESS ME PROPERLY, SLAVE!

IT'S A SAD TALE.

MY STEPMOTHER *PASIPHAË* WAS WITH CHILD.

THE LABOUR HAD BEEN LONG AND PAINFUL. HER SERVANT WOMEN WEREN'T SURE SHE WOULD SURVIVE.

BUT SHE DID AND SO DID HER CHILD. BUT NO ONE EXPECTED HIM TO LOOK LIKE—

—THIS!

MINOS REFUSED TO ADMIT THE CHILD WAS HIS.

IN FACT, HE WAS SO *EMBARRASSED* HE WOULD HAVE *NOTHING* TO DO WITH IT.

MINOS WENT TO THE TEMPLE TO FIND OUT WHAT TO DO WITH THE MONSTER.

HE RECEIVED MANY DIFFERENT SUGGESTIONS.

MOST SAID HE SHOULD DESTROY THE MONSTER, BUT HE COULDN'T DO THAT. HE KNEW THE GODS WOULD CURSE HIM IF HE KILLED HIS OWN CHILD.

29

THE LABYRINTH HAS NEVER BEEN SOLVED. NO ONE EXPECTED THE MINOTAUR TO WORK IT OUT.

BUT *DAEDALUS* TOLD ME THE ONLY WAY TO SOLVE THE PASSAGES.

HERE!

TAKE THIS!

THIS?

WHAT AM I SUPPOSED TO DO? KNIT A MAP?

NO SILLY, YOU TIE ONE END OF IT TO THE ENTRANCE AND LET IT PLAY OUT BEHIND YOU.

THEN YOU ONLY HAVE TO FOLLOW IT BACK TO GET OUT.

I DON'T WANT ANYONE ELSE TRAPPED IN THERE EVER AGAIN.

I HAVE TO GO. THE GUARDS WILL BE HERE SOON.

I'VE BEEN HERE LONG ENOUGH TO KNOW THEIR SCHEDULE.

WAIT!

I NEED TO KNOW—

—WHY ME...?

INTO THE LABYRINTH

*T*HE NEXT DAY, *THESEUS* WAS TAKEN TO THE LABYRINTH.

PEOPLE JEERED LOUDLY AS HE WAS PARADED PAST THEM.

HE WAS PREPARED FOR WHAT WAS TO COME.

HE HADN'T BEEN AFRAID WHEN HE LEFT HOME TO GO TO ATHENS—

—HE WASN'T AFRAID NOW EITHER.

HE KNEW HE COULD DEFEAT THIS MONSTER JUST AS HE HAD DEFEATED THE BANDITS—

—NO MATTER HOW MANY OTHERS BEFORE HIM HAD DIED BELIEVING THE SAME THING.

THE BOY YOU SEE BELOW IS RATHER *IMPORTANT*.

THE OTHERS HAVE TOLD MY GUARDS HE IS THE SON OF *KING AEGEUS*.

HE MUST BE *DESPERATE* TO SEND HIS HEIR TO DIE.

WHAT DO YOU THINK, *DAEDALUS?* SHOULD I GIVE HIM AN *INCENTIVE*.

HE IS ROYALTY, AFTER ALL.

KING MINOS, HE IS *YOUR* PRISONER. YOU CAN DO WITH HIM AS YOU WISH.

YOU'RE RIGHT, OF COURSE. YOU'RE ALWAYS RIGHT.

PRISONER!

YOUR FATHER BELIEVES ME TO BE AN *EVIL* MAN. *AND YET* HE SACRIFICES YOU TO DIE IN THE LABYRINTH AT THE HAND OF MY SON.

LET ME MAKE YOU A PROPOSITION.

IF YOU MAKE IT OUT OF THE LABYRINTH...

...ALIVE...

I WILL RELEASE ATHENS OF ITS TRIBUTE AND RELEASE YOU AND THOSE WHO CAME WITH YOU.

IT IS AGREED.

33

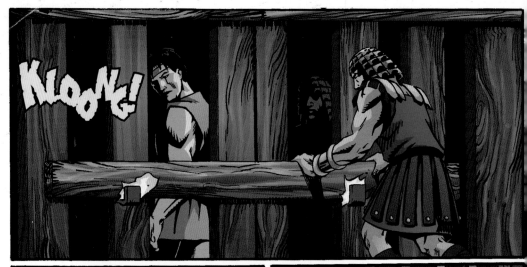

KLOONG!

TAKE THIS! IT'S THE ONLY ONE YOU GET.

BUT IT'S STILL DAYLIGHT.

NOT IN THERE IT ISN'T.

BOOOM!

HERE WE GO.

THESEUS' LUNGS BURNED, HIS RIBS ACHED AND IT HURT TO STAND.

HE HAD GIVEN THE MONSTER HIS BEST SO FAR, YET THE BEAST WOULD NOT STAY DOWN.

TWACK!!

UNH...

GET...
OFF...
ME!

KARACK!

YOU
FOUGHT
WELL.

I WILL MAKE
SURE OUR FIGHT
WILL BE TOLD
FOR AGES.

THOOM
THOOM
THOOM

MINOS!

W-WHAT IS THIS?

W-WHAT DOES HE CARRY?

IT IS THE HORN OF OUR SON...

NOoooooooo!

GUARDS!!

KILL HIM!

FATHER, YOU CAN'T DO THAT.

ARIADNE! BE QUIET!

WHAT?

YOU PROMISED TO FREE HIM.

IF YOU DON'T, THE GODS WILL PUNISH YOU AND CRETE.

SHE IS RIGHT, MY KING.

YOU ARE RIGHT, GIRL.

THE GODS CURSED US BEFORE. THEY WILL AGAIN.

HE IS FREE. YOU ARE FREE. DAEDALUS, I WILL DEAL WITH YOU LATER.

YOUNG HEIR OF ATHENS, YOU HAVE PROVEN YOUR WORTH.

TAKE YOUR PEOPLE AND RETURN HOME.

I RELEASE YOU AND YOUR CITY OF ANY OBLIGATIONS.

44

GLOSSARY

AEGEUS: the king of Athens and Theseus' father

AETHRA: Aegeus' wife and Theseus' mother

APHRODITE: the Greek goddess of love and beauty

ARIADNE: Minos' daughter, who helps Theseus to escape the labyrinth

ATHENS: one of the great historic Greek city-states

CONNIDUS: Theseus' centaur (half-horse, half-human) tutor

CRETE: a large island in the eastern Mediterranean Sea, off the southern coast of Greece

DAEDALUS: the engineering genius who built the labyrinth for King Minos

HERAKLES: a legendary Greek hero; also known by his Roman name, Hercules

LABYRINTH: a place full of confusing passageways and dead ends; a maze

MEDEA: Aegeus' wife

MINOS: the king of Crete and the father of the Minotaur and of Ariadne

MINOTAUR: a ferocious half-man, half-bull; the son of Minos and Pasiphaë

PASIPHAË: wife of Minos, mother of the Minotaur

PERIPHETES: a bandit who preys on travellers along the road to Athens

PITTHEUS: Theseus' grandfather

POSEIDON: the Greek god of the sea

PROCRUSTES: an evil innkeeper who murders his guests by stretching them or cutting off their limbs

SINIS: a sinister bandit who kills his victims by forcing them to hold the tops of two trees at the same time, causing them to be torn apart

THESEUS: son of Aegeus and Aethra; Aegeus' successor as king of Athens

FURTHER READING, WEBSITES AND FILMS

Deary, Terry. *The Groovy Greeks* (Horrible Histories) Scholastic, 2007. An entertaining insight into the lives and culture of the ancient Greeks.

Limke, Jeff. *Jason: Quest for the Golden Fleece* Lerner Books, 2008. Read about the exciting adventures of another great Greek hero, Jason, and his relationship with a certain woman named Medea.

Jim Henson's The Storyteller: Greek Myths. DVD. Directed by David Garfath and John Madden. Hollywood, CA: Sony Pictures, 2004. In this entertaining series of stories, four famous Greek myths - including Theseus and the Minotaur - are brought to life using live actors and puppets.

Myths and legends.
http://myths.e2bn.org/index.php
On this website you can read lots of myths and legends from all over the world. You can also learn about the origins of each of the stories and watch short animations that accompany each one.

Storrie, Paul D. *Hercules: The Twelve Labours* Lerner Books, 2008. Learn about Theseus' hero and inspiration, Hercules, one of Greece's greatest legends.

Woff, Richard. *The British Museum Pocket Dictionary of Ancient Greek and Roman Gods and Goddesses* (British Museum Pocket Dictionaries) British Museum Press, 2003. Find out more about the gods and goddesses of the ancient Greek and Roman civilizations.

CREATING *THESEUS: BATTLING THE MINOTAUR*

To craft this tale for the Graphic Myths and Legends series, author Jeff Limke consulted two of the most famous anthologies of Greek myths, Edith Hamilton's *Mythology* and *Bulfinch's Mythology* by Thomas Bulfinch. Artist John McCrea referenced numerous historical and traditional sources to give the art an authentic look, from classical Greek architecture to the clothing, weapons and armour worn by the characters. Professor David Mulroy ensured historical and visual accuracy.

original pencil from page 15

INDEX

ABOUT THE AUTHOR AND THE ARTIST

JEFF LIMKE was raised in North Dakota, USA. There he read, listened to and marvelled at stories from the day he learned to read. He later taught stories for many years and has written adaptations of them. Some of his stories have been published by Arrow Comics, Caliber Comics and Kenzer and Company. His titles for Graphic Universe include *King Arthur: Excalibur Unsheathed*; *Isis & Osiris: To the Ends of the Earth*; *Thor & Loki: In the Land of Giants*; *Jason: The Quest for the Golden Fleece*; and *Arthur & Lancelot: The Fight for Camelot*. Along the way, he got married, and he and his wife had a daughter who loves to read, listen to and marvel at stories.

JOHN McCREA was born in Belfast, Northern Ireland. He has been drawing comics professionally for nearly twenty years. His work has become well known through comics for both DC and Marvel, including titles for such series as *Judge Dredd*, *Hitman* and *Section 8*. He currently lives in Birmingham, UK.

First published in the United States of America in 2008